Doubles Fun
on the Farm

Developed for Harcourt, Inc., by Gareth Stevens, Inc.
This edition published by Harcourt, Inc., by agreement with Gareth Stevens, Inc. No part of this publication may be reproduced or transmitted in any form or by any means, electronic or mechanical, including photocopy, recording, or any information storage and retrieval system, without permission in writing from the copyright holder.

Requests for permission to make copies of any part of the work should be addressed to Permissions Department, Gareth Stevens, Inc., 330 West Olive Street, Suite 100, Milwaukee, Wisconsin 53212. Fax: 414-332-3567.

HARCOURT and the Harcourt Logo are trademarks of Harcourt, Inc., registered in the United States of America and/or other jurisdictions.

Printed in China

ISBN 13: 978-0-15-360284-9
ISBN 10: 0-15-360284-8

15 16 0940 16 15 14
4500514402

Doubles Fun
on the Farm

by Joan Freese

Photographs by Russell Pickering

Harcourt
SCHOOL PUBLISHERS

Chapter 1:
To the Farm

Max lives in the city. He likes to visit his cousin. Her name is Sara. She lives on a farm.

Max visits the farm often. He likes
to play with Sara. He has fun.

Chapter 2:
Finding Doubles at the Farm

Max goes to Sara's house today. He says hello. Then Max sees a bird. Sara sees one, too.

$$1 + 1 = 2$$

Sara says, "1 plus 1 is 2. A double! A double is adding two numbers that are the same."

Sara has two dogs. They like to play. Max looks at the dogs. He thinks about doubles.

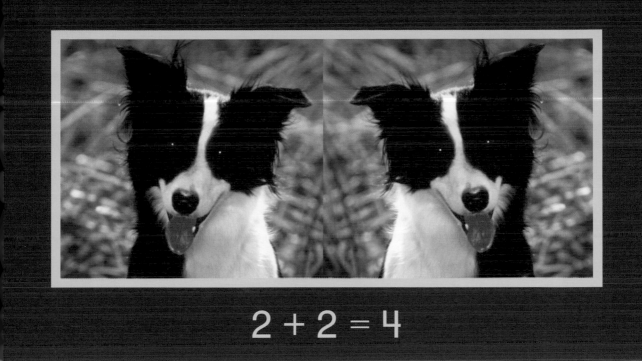

$$2 + 2 = 4$$

Each dog has 2 ears. 2 plus 2
is 4. That is another double.

Sara and Max like to play outdoors.
It makes them hungry. Sara's mom
brings them a snack.

$3 + 3 = 6$

The cousins have crackers.
Sara has 3 crackers. Max has 3,
too. They have 6 crackers in all.
A double again!

The cousins go for a walk,
Sara's mom comes along. They
hunt for clover.

$$4 + 4 = 8$$

Sara finds two plants. Each has
4 leaves! 4 plus 4 is 8. A double!

Max and Sara go to the stream.
They take off their shoes. They
wade in the stream.

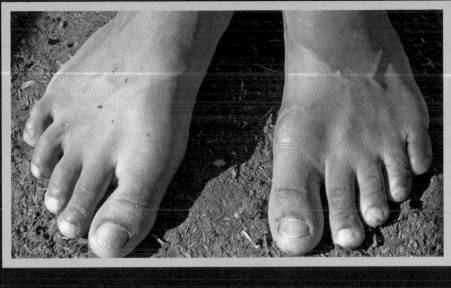

$$5 + 5 = 10$$

"My toes are a double!" Max
says. "I have 5 toes on each foot."
Sara looks at her toes. "Mine,
too," she says.

Chapter 3:
More Doubles Fun

Sara shows Max the garden.
Beans grow there. Corn grows
there. Max likes corn.

$$6 + 6 = 12$$

Sara likes carrots best. She takes
6 carrots. Max takes 6, too. They
give 12 carrots to Sara's mom.

They see chickens. Sara shows
Max how to find eggs.

$7 + 7 = 14$

Sara finds 7 eggs. Max finds 7, too. Another double!

Sara and Max walk home. Sara
sees two spiders. The spiders are
in webs.

$$8 + 8 = 16$$

Max and Sara look. Each spider has 8 legs. 8 plus 8 more is 16. A double!

Chapter 4:
One Last Double

It is almost time to go. The cousins rest. They see an apple tree.

$$9 + 9 = 18$$

Max picks 9 apples. Sara picks 9, too. Max will take 18 apples home. He will think of doubles!

Glossary

add to join two groups

doubles an addition fact in which both addends are the same. $8 + 8 = 16$ is a doubles fact.

equals has the same amount or value

farm land used to grow crops or raise animals

plus added to

stream a small body of flowing water

Photo credits: cover, title page, pp. 3, 6, 8, 9, 10, 12, 13, 15, 16, 17, 18, 19, 20, 21 Russell Pickering; p. 5 National Biological Information Infrastructure; p. 7 © Pinto/ zefa/Corbis; p. 11 © Josh Westrich/zefa/Corbis.